Breaking up w

Breaking up with Christmas is a comical
and nostalgic look at Christmas traditions
from a once young and innocent child, now
a guilt-ridden, standard-driven and
eco-striving Mum.

Is there fresh hope for the relationship
between the embodiment of Christmas and
this devoted Mother? Or, is it staler than a
mince pie in February?

BREAKING UP
WITH
Christmas

LUCINDA WILLICOTT

www.breakingupwith.co.uk

For Mum - who made Christmas look so easy.

My sweaty palms cup my gingerbread latte as I sit in the dark corner of a quiet coffee shop.

I could run out now, if I move swiftly. There'll be other gingerbread lattes, other opportunities to end this ridiculous relationship. I could put this whole break-up on hold for another few months and join in the merriment, infuse everything in the house with brandy and enjoy cleaning up the copious amounts of glitter...

No, no, no this has to stop - now.

Then I hear the sound of sleigh bells. Shit it's early. Christmas comes earlier every year - the bastard. But no, it's not my Christmas coming, the coffee shop is playing a Christmas song. It's bloody October. How dare they sully the sacred scarefest of Halloween with Christmas music? Everyone knows it's Halloween first. If we don't respect the sanctity of the holiday order system then what will become of us? As soon as the first of December arrives then the full force of Christmas will reign down upon us and we will cower under the twinkly pressure it bestows. In December, I will wake up at 4am mumbling "present for the teacher". In December, I will pay more for next-day delivery than the gift is worth. In December, I will chastise my children for being too wild when it is me who has filled them to the brim with excitement and sugar. And why do I put myself through all this torment? All for the sake of one bloody day - Christmas Day.

Oh, I'm all ablaze now. This break-up is back on. I'll shove that Christmas pressure right up your sooty chimney, wrap you so tightly with twinkly lights you can barely smell the cinnamon, force your gullet open and ram you so full of spiced fruit that no amount of antacid can save you. You've messed with me for too long now Christmas - it's over.

As I hug my gingerbread latte tighter, I sadly realise that it too belongs to Christmas, and somehow gingerbread latte has slipped onto the permanent coffee shop offering. This break-up is going to be messy, there's no doubt about it.

Then I hear it, the familiar "Ho Ho Ho" - Christmas has officially arrived. As my eyes sweep its tired and dusty figure, I wonder when Christmas started to look like this. The lights are tangled, the batteries have run out of the singing Snowman, baubles hang without their glitter (yet somehow the floor is now covered in the pesky stuff). The whole ensemble is far too small and a thin layer of sweat has soaked into the over decorated Christmas jumper. The smell soon follows the sight - a far from fine bouquet of mouldy loft lingers with overpowering notes of cinnamon and orange (enough to knock out a reindeer or two), oh and not to forget the ever-present whiff of stale sprouts.

Christmas orders a hot chocolate with all the trimmings. The most calorific drink ever invented - that is until one adds a shot or three of Irish cream, whisky or brandy. Such sinful additions are how I have managed to get through Christmases lately (and increase a dress size or three - although, I'm not sure how that's happened when calories don't count at Christmas time).

The silence has become unholy. My heart is pounding harder than the little drummer boy, our eyes locked like lovers under the mistletoe and our palms sweatier than a teacher at a primary nativity.

Finally, I break this festive tension, "It's not you, it's me."

Pow - right in the baubles.

Before Christmas has a chance to beg for mercy, I recite my well-rehearsed chorus.

"We had a good run. Christmases used to be filled with such magic and wonder."

It's true - they really were. Nothing in my life (so far) has beaten the pure magic that was Christmas (and I have two children!). It would start in October (I know, I know), my mum would dust off the 12" Christmas originals (no covers here) and Elvis, Cliff Richard and Boney M would signal the build up. The foil decorations hung from every crevice of our terraced home would be a sure indication of an imminent visit from 'you know who'. A huge, moulded, plastic Father Christmas (not Santa - never Santa) face hung in our dining room - watching us as we ate. His chubby finger pointed at his nose - "I know if you've been naughty - I know if you've been nice." There was an obvious sign that Christmas was corrupt right there, you know naff-all about me, Christmas and that's one of the reasons we are breaking up. You never tried to really get to know me.

"I'm different now, Christmas."

I'm not 5 years old anymore. I'm a 39-year-old mum, with two young children, a demanding job and a set of standards so high even the Angel Gabriel can't reach them. I get it: Christmases aren't about me anymore. I'm not the one in awe at the stocking I put at the end of my own bed. Christmas is about my two innocent little cherubs, whom I am willingly contracted into creating a magical, memorable experience for. I am so lucky to have children to create all this magic and wonder for. I spent so long imagining what Christmases would be like with a family, I was not at all prepared for the reality. Magic and wonder don't just turn up at the door, they have to be crafted, created and contrived. It takes a whole lot of energy and resource, of which I have come to the conclusion it is not worth.

Plus, you, Christmas, have not changed - you remain the same. You haven't evolved with the times, the world isn't as simple as it once was. You demand we blindly repeat traditions year in year out, which were created centuries ago. Thus draining our energy, our pockets and the planet. This isn't going to be an easy break-up, Christmas, but let's go through this together and let me put forward my case.

CHRISTMAS TREE

"Do you remember how much fun it used to be decorating the tree?"

Unearthing all the Christmas decoration boxes from the loft was such a joy. We didn't mind the lofty smell, we welcomed it like a wet dog or elderly relative. The tree was adorned with:

tinsel
...and stars
.......and beads
.............and baubles
...................and crackers
.............................and glitter
And bows.

Oh, the profuse amounts of glorious glitter. I nearly forgot the lights, the multicoloured twinkly lights, which never worked and Dad would have to fix them every year. Dad took to this task with such joy and delight - he didn't mind fixing them after a long day at work rather than eat his tea and watch the news at 6pm. It was Christmas, after all.

"It's not fun now is it - decorating the tree?"

Now, decorating the tree is letting my six- and two-year-old put over a hundred decorations on one branch of the Christmas tree. To the point where I cannot understand why on God's green earth they keep putting them on that same branch when there is no more room and a whole tree to decorate. Plus there is not just one tree nowadays, there is the tree in the lounge (or the 'main tree'), the tree in the playroom (or 'their tree'), the tree in the kitchen (or the 'extra tree' - as the kitchen didn't feel Christmassy enough) and, of course, the outside tree (or the we love Christmas this fucking much, 'show off' tree).

WRAPPING PRESENTS

"Do you remember matching the wrapping paper to the tree?!"

I remember this Christmas well. I was in my late twenties and it was my 'Homemade Christmas' when I hand-crafted Christmas crackers, stitched beautiful labels and decoupaged baubles. I was in Christmas craft heaven. But I wanted the wrapping paper to match my wonderland so I gleefully frequented each supermarket til I found the right kind of white wrapping with silver snowflakes. Not silver wrapping with white snowflakes - not 'off-white' paper with silver snowflakes - white paper and silver snowflakes. Oh the joy, oh the merriment. Oh the copious amounts of free time I used to have.

"Wrapping the presents got a lot tougher didn't it?"

I'd peaked too soon with my 'Homemade Christmas'. I mean how was I going to top origami napkins - how? Wrapping became more elaborate over the years - posting paper with ribbon weaved by French artisans, chalk paper with bespoke hand-drawn illustrations, drying oranges and foraging for holly... I was wrapping £2 socks in £10 worth of decorations. It had got out of control to say the least.

From last October onwards (in preparation for last Christmas) I scrimped and saved every piece of scrap paper to be used as wrapping paper. Apparently, all this decoration ends up in landfill - shiny paper and (troublesome) glitter is not biodegradable and I had been vastly adding to the world's waste problem. Also not recyclable - sellotape. So my Boxing Day was not spent eating Quaver sandwiches in my new socks watching the CBeebies pantomime for the eighth time. It was spent removing the sellotape from enough scavenged paper to wrap a herd of reindeer. Is it me, or does Christmas and eco living not go hand in hand? We buy shit we don't need, wrap it in shit we don't need and decorate it in shit we don't need.

There are only two things that will survive the slow destruction of the planet, and that's cockroaches and tinsel. Cockroaches will be decorating the planet with the vast amount of tinsel us humans produced using a material that doesn't break down for thousands of years. Why did we create tinsel? To celebrate the birth of Jesus Christ of course. Tinsel was hung all around the stable, and when the angels came down from the heavens they had it attached to their halos and the rim of their gowns. So tinsel is a huge part of the festivities... oh wait, no it's not - it's some treacherous decoration which sheds everywhere and eventually ends up in landfill.

Christmas, you are vastly adding to the world's waste problems with wrapping and decorations alone. You are out of control and it's time to stop.

VISITING FATHER CHRISTMAS

"We used to love visiting Father Christmas each year."

Each year, a few days before Christmas, my mum would take us to pay a visit to our local department store Rossiters, where the big man himself would be waiting for us. Each year it was the same department store and the same Father Christmas (years later we found out it was our secondary school IT teacher, who was also a member of the local theatre group). We never questioned if it was the real Father Christmas, because it WAS the REAL Father Christmas (what are you trying to say, that a man with a combined passion for computing and teaching was under that suit?! How absurd). He wore a fake beard and a baggy suit, and we never questioned his validity as Father Christmas. Never.

"Father Christmas visits have become trickier."

My daughter can sniff out a fake beard. Her x-ray vision can spot the stuffing plumping up their belly and her sonar can detect a cheap, rented suit. But, she is too smart to call us out on this lie. She knows if there are no Father Christmas visits there are no extra presents, so she goes along with the charade for the sweet bounty. She has rationalised this confusion with the badly dressed Father Christmases being the real Father Christmas's helpers and then the really good ones (and we've had some crackers) being the real deal.

The confusion is my fault entirely. As children we saw the same Father Christmas every year so had nothing else to compare it too. As a greedy parent basking in the Christmas wonder emanating from my child's innocent eyes, I whisked her to every garden centre, farm and department store who hosts an audience with Big Red. She in turn now knows a thing or two about how a Father Christmas should appear. We have even gone so far as to rank them:

#3 - In third place is the 'Christmas helper' from the farm. Rather than his suit being tarnished with ashes and soot it was tarnished with brown sauce from his BLT breakfast bap. His eyes didn't twinkle, they in fact rolled into the back of his head when I asked for a selfie.

#2 - In second place was the department store 'Christmas helper'. His cheeks were more drawn and tired rather than looking like cherries.

#1 - And in first place, the 'real' Father Christmas was... from the ninth floor of the department store. His real beard was indeed as white as snow and his belly did indeed shake like a bowl full of jelly.

Why is Father Christmas always located at a tucked away farm, busy garden centre or the ninth floor of a department store? It would be so much more convenient if Father Christmas visited somewhere our family frequents more regularly like our local supermarket, the park outside school or a petrol station? Oh, actually, on second thoughts scrap that. A large man in red running round a park with a sack, or loitering around a dingy petrol station off the A38 only screams danger - call 999.

BUYING PRESENTS

"All those presents and not one of them I had to think about buying..."

The sound of the gentle, yet deep mass of thin, tissue-like paper is so distinct. The crisp, earthy smell sits in harmony with the smooth, cold pages. This holy book bestows the greatest Christmas power of all. For he who knows the secrets inside could provide a Christmas so wondrous and bountiful, that all of heaven would stop and take heed of this festive miracle...

Circling the Argos catalogue was a Christmas ritual. With one eye on the telly watching Jet taking down another contender, and another on a pair of Elizabeth Duke gold-plated set of hooped earrings, circling that seven-digit number was both productive and satisfying. However, one had to be swift with matters, as this was a well coveted book and if left unattended would be whisked out of sight, leaving me twiddling my ink-stained fingers. "Why did you only pick up one?" I hear you ask. They were free of course, but, like the Holy Bible, they were also bloody heavy.

"Buying Christmas presents has become trickier now hasn't it?"

To ensure a magical Christmas morning worthy of a John Lewis advert I ashamedly start my Christmas shopping in July. Sadly come Christmas, the faddish presents I bought in the summer aren't always the hit they would have been 6 months ago. This is the price they pay for wanting, and I quote "my stocking to be taller than me, Mamma!". Your wish is my command you spoilt little shits. From July onwards I note every "Can I have" and "I really need" and slowly my airing cupboard becomes the cave of wonders. My extremely early gift purchasing applies to my husband too. He has been lucky enough to receive:

#Egg poachers
[Frustrated Husband] "I cannot contain these egg whites, we need special egg poaching containers!"
[Me - quietly to myself whilst sniggering] "What you need, my precious fool, is an egg poacher. I could pick one up at the supermarket tomorrow along with your Valentine's card, but with Christmas only 10 months away this is a prime stocking filler... jingle all the way..."

#Toaster bags
[Frustrated Husband] "The grill takes too long to make a cheese toastie, we need a grill for the bottom as well as the top!"
[Me - quietly to myself whilst sniggering] "What you need, my moronic beloved, are toastie bags - a toaster will heat the

bread both sides. I could pick this up from the supermarket tomorrow along with the children's Easter eggs, but with Christmas only 8 months away this is a prime stocking filler... we wish you a merry Christmas..."

#Coconut scrubbing pads
[Frustrated Husband] "I know you're all eco and don't want to buy any more scourers, but these eggs are stuck on tight to this pan. What we need is a pressure washer for dishes!"
[Me - quietly to myself whilst sniggering] "What you need is an environmentally friendly scrubbing pad, you simpleton. I could order this to be delivered tomorrow along with our reef-safe sun lotion, but with Christmas only 6 months away this is a prime stocking filler... oh I wish it could be Christmas everyday..."

#Ladel
[Frustrated Husband] "Our spoons are too small to scoop out these eggs, we need a big egg scooping spoon."
[Me - quietly to myself whilst sniggering] "What you need, my dearest halfwit, is a ladle. I could pick this up from the supermarket tomorrow along with the children's school plimsolls, but with Christmas only 4 months away this is a prime stocking filler... dashing through the snow..."

#Lint Remover
[Frustrated Husband] "The dog has sat on my suit and his hairs are everywhere! What we need is a small hoover that can suck dog hair off garments!"
[Me - quietly to myself whilst sniggering] "What you need,

my beautiful buffoon, is a lint remover. I could pick this up from the supermarket tomorrow along with the children's Halloween masks, but with Christmas only 2 months away this is a prime stocking filler... it's beginning to look a lot like Christmas..."

Egg poachers, toaster bags, a ladle, coconut scrubbing pads and lint remover. All hits no fillers... and largely egg related...

My daughter has questioned how Father Christmas can fit all these goodies in his sleigh with all the other children's presents. I explained it's the same as how Amazon Prime can receive, process, dispatch and deliver my new electric toothbrush all in one night - with well-executed processes and procedures. Or as I call it - 'magic'. Unfortunately, this time my usual 'magic' answer was just not cutting it. We told her some of these presents were from Mama and Dada. "Which ones?" she questioned. "Why are they in the same wrapping paper?" "Urmm...I...hmmm..." I had ran out of answers. I was in too deep without a safe word. I simply popped a chocolate digestive in her mouth and mumbled something about not answering questions on Christmas Day. From then on we decided to differentiate our presents: the ones from Father Christmas would be ornately wrapped by the high elf himself. These presents would be from the small list written to Father Christmas (he can fit no more than five per child in his sleigh). The Christmas presents from us would be wrapped in paper I scavenged from parcels and from inside shoes. The difference was clear. The effort was ridiculous.

So that's the children sorted. Now what about the adults? I can't give them framed photos of the children again... can I? What about my 88-year-old neighbour and Great Grandma who is allergic to everything? Every year I rack my brain as to what heartfelt gift would be enjoyed or even cherished. This is where I long to hear those sacred words, "Shall we not do presents for each other this year?" Oh the relief, the grateful release from this woeful Christmas ritual. "Fuck me, yes." I am but a mortal who kneels before those who are brave enough to summon this kindest of gestures. For suggesting we not partake in the exchanging of gifts could present itself as mean, cheap or lazy. But it couldn't be further from the truth. We are bound to an outdated tradition which encourages us to purchase items for each other we do not need or want. So thank you to those who are strong enough to simply suggest we pass on this particular tradition - I hope to, one day, be as bold and brave as you.

The final knife in the present-buying-back is eco living. We are desperate to be as environmentally friendly as possible and I'm not about to throw my beliefs into landfill just because of bloody Christmas. So this means no presents from the 'Book of Argos'. If it's not wooden, then it's second-hand from the 'App of eBay' (apart from the presents from Big Red - I cannot imagine explaining that to my ever-questioning six-year-old). This adds an extra element of fun to the present buying process:

#1 Bidding for presents
#2 Paying more than the present's worth originally

#3 Losing presents at the last minute

#4 Hoping the presents arrive

#5 Hoping the presents arrive as described

#6 Cleaning the presents (yes, I have to clean my children's Christmas presents)

From July onwards I am on high alert as any minute my phone alarm might go off signalling the beginning of a bidding war for an overpriced, retired, Lego set with missing pieces.

GIVING AND RECEIVING PRESENTS

"The joy of present opening use to be intoxicating..."

I distinctly remember that as children we were allowed to
open one present Christmas morning from our stocking.
This could be done before we woke our mum and dad, no
matter what time it was - so it had to be a good one. Each
present was carefully felt and fondled by our greedy little
fingers. No wrapping was ever harmed, no bow creased or
label torn - we were good children who obeyed the holy rules.
One Christmas I felt what I was sure was a Lady Lovely Locks
doll - I tore into that wrapping paper like only a seven-
year-old could, only to reveal a furry pencil case and key
chain. For two hours my sister silently paraded her Sylvanian
Families figure set in front of me whilst I disappointedly
zipped and unzipped my pencil case. Where did I go so
wrong? It was easy to be fooled, there were a lot of 'non gifts'
in that stocking. I knew Father Christmas believed strongly
in oral hygiene and that's why each year we received a new
toothbrush and toothpaste. He liked us to be sparkly from
head to toe, with new underwear and socks. Not too sure
what his angle was though on the toilet roll and washing-up
liquid? However, he made up for it with a multi-bag of crisps

- God bless you Father Christmas - God bless you. All great little treats, but somehow in my selfish, ungrateful, spoilt, little mind these 'non gifts' were all hurdles to unwrap before I got to the good stuff.

"Giving presents just isn't what it used to be..."

If Father Christmas put a toothbrush in my daughter's stocking she would raise the question of Father Christmas's financial affairs. She would enquire as to the state of his mental capacity and disregarding all my answers she would conclude she had been naughty and this 'non gift' was a form of punishment. There are no fillers in my children's stockings just hits. These entitled little brats (of my creation) just wouldn't allow it.

The speed in which my daughter races through her presents is worthy of an Olympic medal. Once the starter gun is fired, she's off, making light work of sellotape, ribbons and bows. We advise her to slow down, but she's on a winning streak with hit present after hit present. The adrenaline is flowing through her veins and she will take home the gold this Christmas. Months of present buying, cleaning and wrapping are over within half an hour, begging me to question the effort vs satisfaction ratio.

What is the right amount of presents a child should receive anyway? What would that be measured in? Grams, metres, litres, tog? What we need is a 'Christmas Spirit Level'. A

'Christmas Spirit Level' is a similar device to a normal spirit level (which is used to ensure a surface is level). A 'Christmas Spirit Level' however, would be used to measure the correct amount of presents for your child. Too few gifts and the little bubble would descend down the spirit tube, indicating your child will be disappointed with their haul. The little bubble inclining too far up the spirit tube would indicate too many presents resulting in a spoilt brat. What you are trying to achieve is the perfect level of presents which will result in a strait-laced child - grateful enough to appreciate their lot, but still feels special and lucky. As there is no such thing as a 'Christmas Spirit Level' to date, my six-year-old demanded her stocking was taller than her - so I outwitted her by presenting small gifts in larger boxes. Yes, I can outsmart a six-year-old... for now.

Presents, both giving and receiving, used to be the Christmas activity which gave me the most joy - but now it is more challenging than finding a friendly innkeeper on Christmas Eve. Present buying is one of the main reasons for this break-up.

ELF ON THE SHELF

"We had the original elf on the shelf."

We didn't have an elf on the shelf per se. We had a large moulded, plastic Father Christmas face that hung on the wall in our dining room. Big Red's finger was resting on his nose, letting us all know he was watching us - he was always watching us. Father Christmas was collating his list of naughty children, of which we could be one. That large, plastic reminder was all that was needed to keep us in line. I don't remember my mum using the "be good or he won't come" threat. It just wasn't needed.

"I have my own personal Elf to keep the festive pressure high."

The Elf works as an additional reminder for my children to be good, otherwise he'll report back to Big Red that they're being a shit and they'll (quite rightly) receive a lump of coal. This fits perfectly with my parenting philosophy (blame others when disciplining my children, "The Elf is watching you as well as Father Christmas, you are surrounded, so be good or risk no Christmas presents. I, however, would never withhold Christmas presents, because you're my babies and I love you more than all the peppermint whisky in the world").

The children have an 'Elf on the Shelf' to keep their hijinxs in line during the festive period. I am lucky enough to have the lesser known, but ever-present 'Elf on Oneself' which keeps the festive pressure constantly flowing. My Elf works similarly to the children's Elf. Wherever I am throughout December the tricksy Elf springs into my mind sparking festive panic and pressure. My mischievous Elf particularly likes to pop up and surprise me in the shower, when I'm in a meeting at work and of course at 4am. My cheeky Elf likes to remind me about all the things I have yet to do before the big day, like wrap the table presents, raid the dressing-up box for anything that will pass as adequate Shepherd's attire and find and clean the 'nice' dinner plates. My naughty Elf also enjoys exploding guilt bombs throughout December resulting in me purchasing a stocking full of presents for the dog, decorating the car with tinsel and renting a snow machine so my children can have a white Christmas. As long as I comply with my lively Elf the dusting of guilt will eventually disappear and the panic and pressure will dim.

I don't need my very own Elf sprinkling worry and shame all over me during this festive season. 'Elf on Oneself' is just not required, now take your bag of guilt bombs and bugger off.

CHRISTMAS CARDS

"I use to love receiving Christmas cards."

At primary school receiving Christmas cards was a mark of how popular I was. I couldn't wait for Mrs Ellison to open the Christmas letter box at the end of the day and dish out the cards. I remember telling my mum how popular I was and everyone must like me. It had nothing to do with the fact that I sent out a card to everyone in the class on 1st December. My mum couldn't be prouder of her first-born as she rummaged for more string to display my popularity in card form.

"Christmas cards have become an utterly pointless exercise."

When my daughter came home from school with a dozen Christmas cards I promptly encouraged her to reply:

[Mama] "Write your Christmas cards to your friends, darling."
[Daughter] "Why, what's the point?"
[Mama] Huh? "Because they have sent one to you."
[Daughter] "Yes, but it seems a lot of effort to go to to wish them 'Merry Christmas'."
[Mama] Well, she has got me there.

[Daughter] "Can't I just say 'Merry Christmas' to them, why do I need to make a card?"

[Mama] Bloody hell yes you can, that would cut out a lot of effort and forced fun.

[Daughter] "Plus, aren't Christmas cards made of cut down trees and isn't that bad for the environment?"

Blimey, generations of tradition has just been culled by a six-year-old who is utterly correct. Why am I forcing her to send 30 cards when she can merely look them straight in the eye, shake their hands and wish them glad tidings? Christmas cards in this situation do seem a little ridiculous. I can spot a battle I don't want to pick a mile off and when my six-year-old has a perfect argument I am more than happy to wave the white flag in surrender.

Christmas cards aren't completely redundant, I still post cards to friends who I don't see regularly. Why I do this at the busiest time of year and not at say, Easter or Halloween, a far quieter holiday, I don't know.

In the blissful haze of motherhood and steered by my blinding pride for my children, I have ensured their faces are printed on the family Christmas card each year. My children are, and forever will be, the most beautiful children to have ever sat under a (main) Christmas tree and everyone in my address book will be lucky enough to receive one of these prestigious cards. Before our children came along our dog was the most beautiful pet to have ever sat under a (main) Christmas tree and was printed on our cards - we just got very lucky to be blessed with such beautiful creations (I realise that everyone thinks their children are the most beautiful, but ours ACTUALLY are!). However, creating this masterpiece photo card is far from easy. The dog would sit dribbling with treats under his nose (but out of shot). My daughter would be brought to tears as she was forced to sit still for a few mere minutes (it really was only a few minutes). Our last sitting was the most absurd with me exuberantly announcing, "Look I have a poo poo on my head - can you see it? Mama poo poo, Mama poo poo! I'm going to throw the poo poo at you! Mama poo poo, Mama poo poo! Oh no poo poo is coming out of my ears! Mama poo poo, Mama poo poo! Look I'm picking the poo out of my ears and eating it! Mama poo poo, Mama poo poo!" How undignified. The idea that my children find that funny at all is shameful. However, it got the desired effect. I have a Christmas photograph worthy of the cover of 'Parenting at Christmas' magazine (if there is such a thing) and no tears were shed - by the children at least.

OFFICE CHRISTMAS PARTIES

"All those office Christmas parties..."

Poring over the Christmas party menu was certainly a little Christmas bonus 'should I have the garlic mushrooms, or prawn cocktail starter? Chocolate cheese cake, or Christmas pudding?' The corners of that menu were well and truly moist and dog-eared by the time I'd finished with it. My decision would take weeks to reach and was a contract I would not enter into lightly. I would eat every morsel of my Christmas meal - mince pie, coffee and all. My decisions would need to count. Never did I dance at a Christmas party - after the meal I would be found hiding in a corner, stuffed and ashamed, secretly undoing the button on my new, spangly River Island low riders. I knew all the loop holes, wear a loose top, don't eat lunch (you'll need all the room) and take the sick bowl to bed (I never needed it but the howls my stomach made just couldn't be trusted).

"Where are they now?"

Have the parties disappeared? Do colleagues still fear the office weirdo with the mistletoe? Does everyone load up on the free table wine? Do the boss's dance moves still empty the dance floor? Is there still that one lonely girl licking the plate of her sixth course sneakily undoing the top button on her River Island low riders? And what happened to the menus... tell me of the menus?

Even if Christmas parties still existed I wouldn't know about them. I'm snug as a bug by 10pm and the thought of having to put on a spangly dress and have an adult conversation past 8pm is frightful. Even a free, six course meal couldn't drag me from my sad, safe, little routine - more so than ever at Christmas time when I've got a to-do list longer than my reel of ribbon weaved by French artisans (a list which I insist on adding to at 4am). Funnily enough I am not in the mood for free table wine and office banter at Christmas time.

CHRISTMAS CRAFTS

"Christmas crafts - good wholesome fun!"

Christmas crafts were mainly enjoyed at school. The only
craft we were allowed to do at home as children was painting
and that was done outside on a sunny day. To keep frostbite
at bay we left the glue sticks, glorious glitter and crate paper
at school.

"Christmas crafts are just forced fun."

I did feel slightly robbed by my mum's lack of Christmas
crafting enthusiasm. Ready to remedy this I partnered up
with Pinterest, who boasted a board full of Christmas crafting
creations. I was confident that this wholesome Christmas
activity would not only stretch our collective creative skills,
but provide that warm, fuzzy feeling that only glueing cotton
wool on bright red felt can bring. Our fridge door would
soon be adorned in shiny, glittery Christmas artwork. When
the children returned from school each day the table would
be craft ready to create their Christmas masterpieces. At
first the children enjoyed coming home to see what I'd set
up, but after a few toilet roll Christmas trees, cotton wool
snowmen and lollipop snowflakes they grew tired and this
added merriment turned into a chore. I would guilt them

into participating with, "You can only do Christmas crafts at Christmas time". And ashamedly, "Father Christmas might see this as naughty behaviour". I was kidding no one. This was forced Christmas fun and the game was up. In the end I didn't have the energy to coerce them into taking part and furthermore energy to clean up the endless amounts of glitter. Pinterest had broken its Christmas promise of a fridge full of festive artwork. All I was left with was some googly eyes and pom-poms sliding off an over-glued cardboard reindeer, and of course the mess...

Glitter remains dormant for 11 months of the year, but during December it wreaks havoc. My relationship with this crafting medium has changed from friend to foe. Like a beloved Christmas helper it turns my children's scribbles into sparkly, festive masterpieces. However, this helper doesn't want to lie dormant for 11 months of the year and has turned rogue. Now glitter is a pure menace and lodges itself into every crack and crevice of home, man and beast. I can still be found removing glitter from the depth of our couch well into the summertime. No one is safe from this pest.

GINGERBREAD HOUSE

"Christmas baking was delicious."

My mum's baking was delicious all year round, but it had an extra sparkle at Christmas time. Although my mum never attempted a gingerbread house, her Christmas cupcakes (regular cupcakes with silver sprinkles on) and Christmas chocolate cornflake cakes (regular chocolate cornflake cakes with silver sprinkles on) were the talk of the neighbourhood. I was once ushered into my friend Natasha's house, where her mum presented me with her chocolate cornflake cakes and asked my opinion. Taking one look at them I knew my mum had nothing to worry about. It was a pitiful offering and I was only too happy to give my criticism. Natasha's mum's chocolate cornfakes cakes were shit because:

THERE WAS NO CHOCOLATE ON THEM AND SHE USED SHREDDIES INSTEAD OF CORNFLAKES.

The two key ingredients you need for chocolate cornflake cakes are in the title. What you presented to me that day, Natasha's mum, was an abomination.

"I can see why my mum didn't attempt a gingerbread house."

Ever aspiring to raise standards and push the boundaries of my patience and baking skills, I decided baking a gingerbread house from scratch was for us. I wanted the lens flared, gentle lighting as we threw icing sugar in each other's faces. I wanted the soft focus and extreme close-ups as we comically constructed gingerbread figures. I had vision, I had expectations - and they were high. Building a gingerbread house was going to be a joyous new tradition that would showcase our love for each other and Christmas. Why don't more families make a gingerbread house? I mean how hard can it be? I have a degree from the University of Exeter and have birthed two children. Of course I can make a fucking gingerbread house.

I can't make a fucking gingerbread house. Who the fuck can make a gingerbread house? Why are the walls different sizes? I cut the dough to the same size. Why don't the walls slot in together? I made grooves. Why doesn't the icing glue stick it all together? It's supposed to be baking cement. Why is the icing glue all over my two-year-olds face? We have no icing glue left. How do you put the piping bag together? Nothing's coming out. Now everything's coming out. Where's the roof? Shit, I forgot to make a roof. Our gingerbread house has no pissing roof. Fuck me.

Our gingerbread house was re-branded an ancient gingerbread ruin. It was saved by the generous dusting of icing which turns any disastrous Christmas bake into a snowy masterpiece. Icing, it seems, is the glitter of the baking world. Turns out what you need to make a gingerbread house is not a BA Hons from the University of Exeter but training and subsequent qualification granted by the Sugar Plum Fairy herself.

The gingerbread ruin was nibbled here and there over the next few days. First the people were missing, then the trees and fences, then the side walls, until all that was left was the front wall propped up by cocktail sticks. No one admitted they'd had so much as a crumb, leaving its disappearance a complete mystery.

We have not attempted a gingerbread house since that Christmas. We clearly failed SPFS (Sugar Plum Fairy School) and I do not have the patience or baking skills to ever undertake a gingerbread house again. So, fuck you Sugar Plum Fairy - I guess I won't be having my gingerbread house and eating it (secretly).

FATHER CHRISTMAS

"I should have stayed broken up with you when I found out you'd been lying and mocking me behind my back. I trusted you, I was too young and innocent to know any better and you broke my heart."

I didn't get told that Father Christmas wasn't real. My parents couldn't bear to see the pain and despair in my 12-year-old eyes. Instead, one cold January afternoon as I was playing on the stairs (we didn't have a big house - the stairs were a place we were encouraged to play) my sister brazenly asked if 'he' was real. Before I had chance to prepare myself, my mother briskly answered "No." "Didn't think so" my sister retorted smugly, and continued playing with her new Polly Pocket like the Christmas realist she was. For me the shock was crushing - I clung to the banisters for emotional and physical support. All those lies, all that deception, and whose lap was I encouraged to sit on each year?

I couldn't distinguish between reality and fantasy. So if Father Christmas was not real, then who looked after all the elves and the reindeer then? Oh, I see, they were lies too. Who crept into our rooms and left all those gifts at the end of our bed? I mean, our parents love us, but I think it's more realistic that a jolly man in a red suit squeezes down our non existent chimney and leaves us presents than our mum and dad having the money and energy to buy and wrap that lot?

So there was no naughty or nice list, there was no mystical child who got coal? That did make a lot of sense as Nathan Pane (the school bully) got a NES one year and I had to save all my birthday and pocket money for two years for a NES with Super Mario 1 as apparently Father Christmas only made those for 'special' boys and girls - BULL...SHIT.

Hang on a minute... hold onto your baubles. Reindeer are real, they're not fictional like dragons and llamas? But can they fly...?

I was hurt and shaken, every part of Christmas felt like it was tainted with fabrication and deceit. For the next few Christmases I was guarded and wary. Christmas had broken my heart and I wasn't about to forget that in a hurry.

"I am a part of that lie now, aren't I Christmas? Your henchman, your executioner, your wingman. You create the lie and I wrap it and place it neatly under the (main) Christmas tree."

I'm not a progressional parent. My pretentious first-born can't be the smug one informing her peers that Father Christmas is a lie. I'm just not that brave. Us weak-willed parents need to keep all those who believe (maybe up to the age of 12) well behaved from October to December. We need the 'He won't leave you any presents' threat. I'm not the one being mean, that jolly fella in red is the unfair one - not letting you paint on the walls... the dick.

With Christmas pressure mounting and the desire to keep my little darlings as young as possible for as long as possible I have been forced to go to extremes to ensure this charade is believable. My dog eats the end of the carrot so it looks like a reindeer has nibbled it. A trail of magic dust (red glitter - a true pest, but in this instance required) leads them from their stockings to the chimney. An imprint of a sleigh can be found in our patchy grass (or 'Christmas crop circles' as my husband likes to call it)...

Now I am a part of this inherited charade and I see the magic and wonder in my children's eyes, I realise why parents partake in this illusion. I would rather have loved and lost Father Christmas than never to have loved him at all.

CHRISTMAS AT SCHOOL

"Christmas at school used to be fun didn't it?"

Christmas at school was so simple - Christmas crafts, Christmas dinner, Christmas nativity, Christmas mufti (non uniform day) and Christmas games day. No fuss just fun. My mum loved nothing better than receiving my over glittered Christmas crafts (my mum loved glitter). She loved washing my crusty dressing gown and choosing a stain-free tea towel for my important role in the nativity.

"I suppose Christmas at school is still fun, but mainly because I don't have to do the work."

Let me take you back to a previous nativity. My daughter is one of twelve angels. I won't have to buy a costume, there must be something we can put together...

• We have pink fairy wings - well that's a start. It'll be fine, I'm not buying a costume.

• We have a white netted mini skirt meant for an 18-year-old adult. I'll put a peg in the back. It'll be fine, I'm not buying a costume.

• I have a white top with Peppa Pig on it - Peppa is the symbol of Christmas isn't she? It'll be fine. I'm not buying a costume.

- Angels wear a halo... how about a white floral headband? It'll be fine. I'm not buying a costume.

- How about a dress made from a white pillow case? Oh, how does dribble stain every white pillow case? It'll be fine. I'm not buying a costume.

- Glittery shoes still two sizes too big for her, she'll only have to wear them for an hour. It'll be fine. I'm not buying a costume.

Oh shit, my wallet seems to have fallen open and my credit card details seem to have accidentally fallen into the Marks and Spencer website and I have bought an angel costume, and it WILL be fine.

I love watching the school nativity. Nothing says Christmas like 60 school kids all mumbling the carol 'Little Donkey' out of tune and out of time. Every year I scour the stage to find the nose picker, the nose-pickers victim (they're usually very close), the repetitive waver, the over enthusiast, the over enthusiast's victim (a shiner for Christmas Day is what all mothers want), the thumb sucker and the one who just refuses to take part. And that's just the teachers... ba dum chhh!

You can always spot my daughter, she will be the one in the costume two sizes two big. I don't know why I buy costumes too big - it's not like she needs the growing room. The costume will be worn once and disregarded immediately. And not because it's special just for the nativity, alas no, because like all costumes it has been cursed with the itches. The finest designer can create the most elegant of gown, but if it has the cursed itches then she will not wear it. She has been heavily encouraged to wear the costume for the duration of the nativity for if not, Father Christmas might deem this naughty behaviour. But once her part has been played her costume hits the floor faster than the needles of a Blue Spruce on Christmas Eve.

I have to say I still love school at Christmas time. My children get into the Christmas spirit and some other poor fool has to do all the hard work.

[Daughter] "Mama, can I wear my Christmas jumper for Christmas jumper day please?"
[Mama] "Yes, your Christmas jumper from last year still fits (the benefit of buying clothes too big)."

[Daughter] "Mama, can I have £1.50 for Christmas dinner please?"
[Mama] "Yes, if I give you a fiver can you bring a couple home for your dad and me?"

[Daughter] "Mama, can I wear pyjamas to school to watch *The Polar Express* please?"
[Mama] "Yes, if I give you a toothbrush and a pillow you might as well stay the night."

[Daughter] "Mama, can I have £4.50 to see Father Christmas

at the farm please?"

[Mama] "Yes, if I give you a tenner can they take your brother?"

If I could keep Christmas at school I would. As I previously said I don't have to do any of the work. I don't want a messy break-up though, so Christmas at school has to go.

ADVENT CALENDARS

"Advent calendars used to be such a simple affair..."

As a child, opening a perforated cardboard square to reveal
a picture each day used to get me out of bed promptly
throughout December. Exchanging glances with my brother
and sister to see who had the better picture was ridiculous
sibling rivalry. But if you did have the better picture you were
elevated to a position of great virtue and became the envy of
your siblings for the day.

"Advent calendars have got a bit much haven't they..."

This year my children received Lego advent calendars. Each
evening they would open their perforated square to reveal
Lego bricks and instructions to create a small toy. These
were far from the primitive advent calendars we received
as children, but I think this is a natural evolution for the
advent calendar. Without this progression the simple advent
would not survive in this greedy, manufactured environment.
Natural selection has forced it to develop more intricate
gifts to keep this Christmas tradition alive. The Lego advent
year coincided with both sets of grandparents giving our
children the more well-known chocolate advent calendar. As
well as these offerings, our little darlings also demanded the

wooden advent train and advent truck which we provide each year to be filled with goodies. Thus resulting in us having to bring dinner forward an hour so we could fit in all the advent calendar merriment before bedtime. I was elated come December 24th and happily threw all advent calendars in the recycling. Next year I will do as all normal parents do and open their children's advent calendars, eat all the contents, have a cry, hide the evidence and deny there was an advent calendar there in the first place. Another well-evolved species brought to the brink of extinction by human greed and laziness.

CHRISTMAS EVE

"How much fun did Christmas Eve used to be?"

As a child it didn't get any more exciting than Christmas Eve. We didn't want to leave the house in case a blanket of darkness suddenly fell upon us and we weren't in our beds asleep, ready to receive our well-deserved bounty.

"Christmas Eve is a difficult day now - don't you agree?"

My entire Christmas Eve is divided between trying to calm two rabid beasts who are foaming glitter (aka my children) and preparing the house for our honoured guests (both sets of parents plus uncles and aunties and great nan's). Whilst my husband decides this is the very day to start his Christmas shopping (skippity skip, skippity, skip, tra, la, la, la, la). Luckily, as I do EVERYTHING he only has to buy a gift for me which I insist is enough booze to get me through to Easter.

I don't get any sleep on Christmas Eve night. It's the one night of the year I crave my bed after being forced by the children to complete such a long list of pointless rituals. All of which are wrapped around the lie of Father Christmas:

#1 - Spread the reindeer food (otherwise they might not come).

#2 - Put out a mince pie and brandy (a bribe so they'll leave presents).

#3 - Sing around a Christingle (so they know you're wholesome and leave you extra presents).

#4 - Read *The Night Before Christmas* (a story checklist so you know you're ready for the arrival and receive maximum bounty possible).

#5 - Put your stocking on your head and run round frantically (not sure why we do that...).

Every hour, on the hour, our six-year-old will sleepily stagger past her overflowing stocking into our room and enquire if 'he's been'. Too tired to notice he's already frequented our residence we put our daughter back in her bed - every hour, on the hour.

CHRISTMAS TV GUIDE

"Memorising the TV guide was a fun festive challenge."

I'm not sure why, or at what point in my teenage years I thought it was such a good idea to memorise the TV guide. As with all tasks I assigned myself, I took to this challenge with seriousness and commitment. My family began to stop using the guide and asked me instead.

"Lulu, what time is *The Only Fools and Horses Christmas Special* on?"
"4.05pm, Dad."
"Lu, when is *Russ Abbott Christmas Show* on?"
"5.35pm, Christmas Day."
"Lu, what's that programme about TV with lovely Noel?"
"*Telly Addicts,* Mum - on at 7.30pm."
"Lu, when's *The Brittas Empire* on?"
"Boxing Day, 7.30pm."
"Lulu, when did you say *Only Fools* is on again?"
"Bloody hell - 4.05pm, Dad."

I was the original version of Alexa for TV listings.

"Lulu, *ONLY FOOLS...*?"
"I'M NOT SAYING IT AGAIN DAD!"

A very early version of Alexa.

Alexa isn't used much in our house, but at Christmas time the kids wear her out:

"Alexa, tell me a Christmas cracker joke."
"Alexa, tell us the names of the reindeer."
"Alexa, how many more sleeps until Christmas?"

To the latter I would love her to have free rein to answer:

[Read in an Alexa monotone voice] "There are no sleeps until Christmas. Father Christmas is dead. Mother Christmas shot him in the head with a AK-47 rifle. She continued the onslaught and single-handedly murdered 5000 elves and barbecued the reindeer. When questioned she slurred "He took all the credit for Christmas. Every year I organised it all. All he did was one night's work."

Blimey Alexa, that got dark quick. How could you say such hilarious but very cruel things?

Anyway back to Christmas telly - it was smashing. Most of the shows were just the same but with "Christmas" in the title and some Christmas trees ('main' trees I believe) and tinsel draped around the set. But still, *Bruce Forsyth's Christmas Generation Game* was vastly more special than the normal *Generation Game*. *Paul Daniels' Christmas Show* was certainly more glitzy than the normal show and *Christmas Top of the Pops* was far superior to the normal *Top of the Pops*.

Oh, how the Christmas TV guide would tantalise us with a written extract of our TV shows. Oh TV guide you were such a tease. Don't give too much away TV guide or we might not want the whole show. How was the Boswell family in *Bread* going to handle the festivities this year? Was *The Vicar of Dibley* really going to eat all those Christmas dinners? Oh TV guide you were so naughty.

We would blindly follow the TV guide on our journey through Christmas TV. Leading us to our pivotal shows not unlike, the star leading the wisemen to the manger. We would gather round the box and present our offerings of Tango, Quavers and mini meringues. Once seated we would all sit in harmony and soak in the joy and amazement. Thank you Christmas TV guide for lighting the way to a wondrous Christmas tradition which brought the whole family together all under one stable... I mean roof.

"What Christmas TV?"

Christmas TV certainly drew the family together. We only had one TV so we all had to be together in one room at a specific time. There was no pausing, catch-up or on-demand service so we had to soak it all in, in that moment. Nowadays with multiple devices we can watch what we want, when we want, where we want. Thus resulting in a disjointed, unharmonious viewing experience. This presents us with a shift in family dynamics, but if we are all watching something Christmassy, and all basking in the glow of Christmas spirit then what's the real harm? The real problem comes when:

THERE IS NOTHING TO FUCKING WATCH.

Where have all the Christmas shows gone? Where are all
the one-off Christmas specials? The Christmas game shows?
The Christmas tear jerkers? Are they seeking refuge in the
Bahamas? Are they on an international game of hide and seek?
Has Mother Christmas shot them down too??

If the TV shows have disappeared, has that rendered the
TV guide useless, is it just blank ink-less pages? It's like
Christmas TV has ghosted me and I have no idea why. I
memorised the TV guide, does that not show my willingness
to adore and worship you, Christmas TV? You were the easiest
part of Christmas to comply with. Why would you ghost me
like this, why?

AFFORDING CHRISTMAS

"Christmas has always been and will always be expensive."

Even as a child it was hard not to notice Mum's exuberant face as she discovered wrapping paper discounted to 10p in the January sales. A find of Christmas cards discounted to 5p for 100 was a steal, even if they were as thin as toilet paper. Finds like these were too good to pass up on, even if you weren't going to use them for another 11 months. The airing cupboard was deep and bare in January and welcomed the bargains.

It's the same with Mum buying food stamps each week to pay for our Christmas banquet, and buying Christmas presents early. Spreading the cost of Christmas and buying things when she had the money helped to keep the big day manageable. To some extent this logic is ridiculous - it's still the same amount of money, whether it is dripping out of her pockets throughout the year or haemorrhaging it in December - the bottom line is still the same. It is just more palatable not to see the full extent of the damage Christmas does to our bank balance. My siblings and I knew that there was a cost to Christmas, it wasn't bought by magic and wishing, it was bought by careful planning and a keen eye for bargains.

Sadly, money doesn't grow on ('main' Christmas) trees. I see the reflection of the twinkling lights in my children's eyes, feel the guilt rise up in my throat and I can't deny them the full force of Christmas in all its costly wonder. They aren't little for long and I want Christmas to be memorable for them, even if it bankrupts me.

Money is another big reason for breaking up with you, Christmas. Pressurising my mum and now me into managing the Christmas spend throughout the year is a boundary I feel you have massively crossed. Christmas, I want nothing to do with you, or your pressure.

SECRET SANTA

"Secret Santa banter was the best!"

As a teenager working part-time in a sports shop it was safe to say it didn't matter who I got for Secret Santa. I would gleefully snigger all the way to the local sex shop to purchase a giant chocolate willy. Everyone would think I was a bold, comical genius without sexual inhibitions and deep pockets to purchase a solid chocolate penis that large and veiny. Hijinks were fully appreciated by all - I would go down as a dirty, Christmas legend. Bravo, bravo.

"Secret Santa is a dangerous game."

Skip forward five years to my first Christmas at an entry level corporate position. As I put my hand in the biscuit tin to pick out my Secret Santa I knew who I'd get, I knew what name was on that scrap of paper, I was the only one who could be that lucky. You guessed it, I pulled out the boss. This was not the place for dirty hijinks. The head honcho was not going to appreciate a giant chocolate cock in all its veiny glory. Instead of immediately skipping to the sex shop I spent hours mentally playing out each scenario where I presented a different gift and the reactions it would evoke. "Secret Santa is anonymous!" I hear you cry. It's bloody not. It takes approximately 20 minutes for everyone to work out who gave what to who. The clues are clear: the wrapping, the thought put into the gift, and the idiot yelling "Open it the other way!" or "Press the button at the bottom, it makes a noise!". I would have 20 minutes of anonymity before my cover would be blown. My options were to go big or go home. A full-on sex doll with several orifices, or a mug with 'World's Best Boss' printed on the front. If I went with the doll (and my entire body was telling me to do it) I would either go down as a Secret Santa Superstar high-fiving colleagues wherever I went, or spend half a day in Human Resources learning about sexual harassment in the workplace and inappropriate conduct. I was young, scared and naive. Fear got the better of me and I went with the mug. Rarely is there a place in society where Secret Santa works and can be enjoyed by all participants.

Also, maybe it's me, but I find it strange that considering buying a chocolate willy is part of a tradition which is linked to the birth of Christ. I mean, the two aren't directly linked, it's not like the wisemen presented baby Jesus with a gimp mask, a cock ring and a vibrator. We buy presents at Christmas as a symbol of the tributes made to the baby Jesus. We take part in Secret Santa at Christmas time to avoid buying presents for everyone in the office - leaving me with the dilemma of whether I purchase a chocolate willy or not. How can a beautiful gesture of giving a baby presents go so awry?

That is why I suggest I bury any remains of Secret Santa in a distant land to ensure it is hidden forever and its whereabouts will be kept a true secret.

CHRISTMAS JUMPERS

"I don't remember Christmas jumpers?"

I've got nothing... they weren't 'a thing'.

"Where did Christmas jumpers come from?"

Not sure when Christmas jumpers became 'a thing'? I seemed to have missed that Christmas when we inaugurated questionably designed jumpers as a new Christmas tradition. I truly don't remember voting them in. As far as I can ascertain, one must wear the most ridiculously uncomfortable knitwear over the festive period to create maximum merriment and delight. The most over-designed the better, so flashing fairy lights which scald their bearer and blind the viewer is a must. The heavier knit the better to really sweat out those Christmas juices. Lastly, no jumper is complete unless it has the cursed itches which as we all know only renders the jumper wearable for the absolute necessities (ie meet and greet and photo opportunities). Then the jumper will hit the floor faster than an unwanted 'non gift'.

I can think of nothing worse to wear to a Christmas party (or Christmas Day itself) than a knitted jumper. No one wants to see their host's sweat soaking into double knit wool. Now a Christmas long sleeve tee or Christmas t-shirt I could buy into on a practical level, but it still doesn't scream partywear or Christmas Day finest.

Sorry Christmas jumpers, you shouldn't have been here in the first place - you have been impeached.

CHRISTMAS EVE BOX

"Christmas Eve was exciting enough."

As a child, Christmas Eve was the pinnacle of Christmas excitement. We just needed to behave ourselves for one more day and our end of the bargain would be complete. When we awoke the reward would be glorious.

If we were presented with Christmas Eve boxes we might have quite literally self-combust. It would have been too much to take in on what was already the eve of the most exciting day of the year.

"Yeah why not give me another fucking job?"

I mean fuck it right? It's not like I've got my hands full at Christmas time. I'm just kicking around waiting for someone to give me another merry job. Yeah, I'll happily find (or construct, or buy) a beautiful box, fill it with new pyjamas, a new book and a new toy ready for the children to open on Christmas Eve night. No, honestly, I don't have anything else I should be doing. I want to do this. I want to.

Christmas Eve boxes are ludicrous. Not only are they another job, requiring more money and more effort, but I believe they dilute Christmas Day. It doesn't have to be that complicated, you receive your presents on Christmas Day, any gifts before then takes away the excitement of opening your presents - on Christmas Day. The day for opening presents is Christmas Day. Not Christmas Eve, Christmas Day. Christmas - Day.

TWIXMAS

"Twixmas went on forever…"

Twixmas (the brief period of time between Christmas and New Year Eve) was truly blissful. Surrounded by new toys, enough Tango and Quavers to feed the cast of the Nutcracker and no school in sight. My mum on the other hand displayed some strange behaviour - ripping down the Christmas decorations on Boxing Day and shaking a cow bell hysterically yelling, "It's over - Christmas is over for another year!"

I had a full week at home before school started to set up She-Ra's Crystal Castle and I was going to make every minute count.

"Twixmas goes on forever…"

Twixmas (the long, endless void where day and night become one between 'ho ho' time and 'next year might be better' Eve) is truly painful. Surrounded by new toys, too much sugar and no school in sight. I manage to find the light in these dark times gleefully removing the Christmas decorations and maybe humming a gay little tune to keep spirits up.

I have a full week of children at home and no school run, so I am going to use this time to fulfil a lot of daytime drinking.

CHRISTMAS PANTOMIME

"The panto was such a treat after Christmas."

We loved heading to the pantomime. Dressed in our new Christmas outfits with matching hair scrunchies and a new shell suit for my brother. We were ready for all the hijinks and merriment only a pantomime brings. Mum would hand us each a plastic bag containing, crisps, pop and a chocolate bar most of which was devoured before those red, velvet curtains opened. Halfway through, after yelling feverishly at Widow Twanky that the horse was indeed behind her, we were parched. Mum would reveal even more pop and even more chocolate from her giant Mum bag saving us from having to queue for sweet treats in the interval. She really was a well organised and thoughtful mum.

"Getting to the pantomime is an adventure in itself."

"We're late! We. Are. Late!" No one's shoes can be found, the coats are being washed for the new school term and I can only find one single glove. When I completed my backward math to figure out what time we should arrive at the theatre I didn't account for lost attire essential for winter (next time count back an extra 15 minutes to allow for this).

We begin our journey to the pantomime cold and behind schedule. As we set off, demons possess my two, dutiful children. They usually compromise on what to listen to in the car, but their spirits are possessed and they argue feverishly between Peppa Pig and the Moana sound track. As it is now after Christmas my "Father Christmas won't bring you presents" threat has expired, so I merely turn off the stereo, returning to my ancient parenting philosophy of blaming someone else, "The theatre won't let us in if they know you've been squabbling." The rage calms and the demons are banished.

We successfully park the car in the dark, enchanted, car park. The overpowering stench of urine fills us with fear and encourages us to pick up the pace.

As we enter the theatre we encounter the refreshment stall where the young ones are tempted to stray from the path with the alluring smell of popcorn and chocolate. Luckily, my giant Mum bag is armed with enough sweet snacks and fizzy beverages to fend off an evil witch or two (thank you, Mother).

Two fearsome giants block the entrance to the theatre and only golden tickets will ensure entrance. As I reach for the golden tickets I am shocked to find they aren't in my coat pocket. I check my inside coat pocket, the pocket of my dungarees, the chest pocket of my dungarees, the back pocket of my dungarees. I normally love a multi-pocketed outfit - but this slapstick display was panicking me. There were no tickets to be found upon my person. Then I hear a helpful, "They're behind you!" Low and behold there are our golden tickets poking out of my huge Mum bag behind me.

I proudly present our tickets, but the fearsome giants still refuse entry. According to them we cannot pass through the theatre doors until tomorrow. I assure them they are mistaken, and I have indeed got the correct day. Snatching the tickets and peering at the dates, I realise it is me who is incorrect. The inscription on the tickets is clearly marked for tomorrow's show. I grab my heavy Mum bag, children and pride, and march out of the theatre as fast as possible.

Once safely at home, I sit, mulled wine in hand reflecting on the morning's extraordinary journey. I realise that I am not richer for the experience. I am tired, pissed off and did I mention tired? Getting the wrong day is completely understandable when one has the most momentous task of delivering a magical Christmas for all. It's not that I got the dates wrong that bothers me, it's the fact that I have to go through all that rigmarole to get them there again tomorrow. Did I mention I was tired after Christmas? I just want to eat the last remains of the Christmas cake (someone has to - I'm doing my family a favour) and drink (anything and everything) in my sweat pants. Is that too much to ask?

CHRISTMAS MUSIC

"The sleigh bells from the Christmas music still echo in my mind."

With my fingers on 'play' and 'record' on my tape dec, I would be ready to capture the Christmas number one. The DJ would tease us with who the winner might be - it really was anybody's guess. Although, I never would have thought Mr Blobby would have hit the hotspot or Bob the Builder for that matter. The music charts just like everything at Christmas time felt extra special. The Christmas number one really mattered to man, woman and, clearly, toddler.

"Whatever happened to Christmas number one?"

After years of talent show winners stealing the number one crown with their one hit wonders the Christmas number one left me feeling cold. I closed the icy door on the Christmas charts and never looked back. Besides, there is an abundance of classic Christmas songs, it would be greedy to fill my tape decks with more. We all know the heart-warming recipe for a classic Christmas song. Start with a snowy Christmas video, add a dash of sleigh bells, a whole choir (if you can afford one), a pinch of heart-break and serve on an elderly rocker wearing some platforms playing an electric guitar - it has an everlasting shelf life and leaves every palette feeling festive.

There is nothing more heart-warming than Christmas music emanating from a child. Watching my children rehearse for the nativity brings tears to my eyes and pride to my heart. Even if they've got the lyrics wrong...

[Singing 'Away in a Manger']

[Daughter] "The cattle's a logging."
[Mama] "The cattle's logging? Don't you mean 'lowing'?"
[Daughter] "No, Mama, logging, they're doing a poo in the stable. I like my version better."
[Mama] "Of course you do, darling."

[Daughter] "Lay down his fruit bread."
[Mama] "Don't you mean 'Lay down his sweet head'?"
[Daughter] "Why does his head taste sweet? I like my version better."
[Mama] "Of course you do, darling."

[Daughter] "The stars in the night sky."
[Mama] "Don't you mean 'bright sky'?"
[Daughter] "Why would the sky be bright - it's night time? I like my version better."
[Mama] "Of course you do, darling."

[Daughter] "And Fitbit us for heaven."
[Mama] "Wait, Fitbit? Just 'fit', sweetheart, not 'Fitbit'"
[Daughter] "There's no such word as 'fit' it's 'Fitbit'. I like my

version better."

[Mama] "Of course you do, darling."

[Daughter] "Until morning is night."
[Mama] "Don't you mean 'nigh'?"
[Daughter] "What does 'nigh' mean?"
[Mama] "Urm... Hmmmm...I like your version better."
[Daughter] "Of course you do, Mama."

My singing voice has been previously described as that of a turkey being slowly and painfully strangled. To protect those around me I carefully mime 'Happy birthday', I reluctantly hum nursery rhymes to my children, and if I am ever backed into a corner with no escape, I speak the words to a song dutifully with little tune. This is until Christmas comes, when I bellow Christmas carols with gusto and pride. I love the feeling of filling my lungs with air and belting out a hymn or two. I don't mind who I'm with or where I am. Come one, come all and let's all set our turkeys free and sing inharmoniously together.

I will miss the Christmas music. But along with previous ex's possessions (the huge hoodie, his parents, the goldfish we bought together), I will say goodbye to Christmas music gracefully with love in my heart and (mulled) wine in my hand.

CHRISTMAS ADVERTS

"I loved watching the adverts at Christmas time."

Watching the adverts glowing from the TV was mesmerising - I was completely under their control. As a child I was powerless to do anything but comply. I have no idea how the toys made it through the adverts without breaking as their quality was so questionable. But, as I watched each toy being demonstrated I wanted... no, needed those toys in my sack each Christmas. At the end of the advert break I would race to my mum (never my dad, Mum and Big Red controlled Christmas goodies - Dad had the responsibility of the tree lights) and repeat my requests, "Mum, can I have a Rainbow Brite Doll, a Pongo Ball, a Stretch Armstrong, a Waterfall Ring Toss, Moon Shoes, a Polly Pocket, Sylvanian Families, She-Ra Dolls..." I might have received one or maybe two of my requests. But it didn't matter because the adverts' power had worn off come Christmas Day and I had completely forgotten what I'd desperately demanded from my mum to make my Christmas 'The best one ever'.

"A vaccine is required to immunise us against the adverts at Christmas nowadays."

Adverts have little potency to my children throughout the

year. There is no way I'm going to buy my children a tractor that climbs walls or a unicorn that poops glitter (friggin' glitter of all things?!) based on a 20-seconds sales pitch and my children know it (they do not know I start Christmas shopping in July). So adverts for 11 months of the year remain a mild irritant. However, at Christmas time with the promise that Father Christmas can bring the children anything they desire, these adverts develop a powerful venom. This poison lasts throughout December rendering victims powerless to do anything other than comply with their message. This venom has evolved and is now infecting adults too, presenting itself in the form of guilt-ridden charity adverts. Symptoms of this poison are severe guilt and sympathy. The antidote is, as always, money. I am so grateful I won't be spending Christmas in hospital, here's £10, I'm so grateful I am not a homeless dog this Christmas, here's £10, I am so grateful I am spending Christmas in a house, here's £10. I am so grateful I am spending Christmas with loved ones, here's £10. I am grateful I am healthy this Christmas, here's £10. I am grateful I'm not an endangered Nebraskan Salt Creek Tiger Beetle, here's £11.

Strangely though I am thankful for these adverts (even though they score a perfect 10 on the guilt-o-meter) as they keep me grounded at Christmas. They highlight how lucky myself and my family are at a time when one can perhaps get carried away with the nuances of Christmas.

A complete juxtaposition to these charity adverts are the adverts created by superstores. Due to their story arcs, complex characters and emotive tones, instead of calling them adverts we call them 'mini movies'. With Christmas TV deserting us, these sickly, sugary, sweet, short films have fast become a Christmas viewing must. They are highly addictive and incredibly nauseating. Overexposure to too many 'mini movies' can result in sentimental overload. The emphasis on 'mental' as a direct result you will be hugging your (main) Christmas tree, kissing its baubles and ringing the cow bell to tell everyone how much you love them and how above all, you love Christmas. The ring leader of these emotive 'mini movies' is the department store John Lewis. My daughter now believes Mr Lewis is a contender to Father Christmas, and one year she even wrote a Christmas list for Mr Lewis as well as Big Red (just in case the latter was overthrown). I obviously put her straight and reassured her than John Lewis wasn't a real person and wouldn't be in competition with the Big Guy. However, I did like the sound of a handsome, slender, Mr J. Lewis sliding down my chimney in a tailored suit leaving a generous amount of high quality gifts at the bottom of my bed. Who wouldn't?

CHRISTMAS FOOD

"We did have fun with all that food didn't we?"

As a child one of the highlights of Christmas was heading down to Somerfield with Mum's bumper book of stamps she'd been saving all year (£2 each week) with the heavenly promise we could choose whichever pop or multi-pack crisps we wanted.

We got the 'big trolley' and piled it high with 'special' Christmas food. This included mini meringues, a tin of Quality Street, a mini multi-pack of cereal (still to this day I cannot visit a hotel buffet breakfast without being reminded of Christmas), squirty cream and of course our choice of pop (I'd always choose Tango) and multi-pack crisps (Quavers). My mum was at the height of merriment as she shimmied to the counter and laid those stamp cards down like a royal flush. She repeatedly reminded us on the way out that she had spent no money on this feast whilst picking up five more books to start saving for next year's 'free' Christmas banquet. At home she would display the food on the sideboard like prizes at a Christmas raffle. This would be done in November and no one (and I mean no one) was allowed to go near that food until Christmas Eve. We would merely stare at it longingly, misting up the plastic packets until December 24th when anarchy reigned and we would stuff our greedy little faces with Quavers and Tango until we burst.

"The food has got out of control hasn't it?"

In the latest Christmas food catalogue my supermarket
dispatched there were fifteen different mince pie options.
Fifteen. How many ways do we want spiced fruit wrapped
in shortcrust pastry? I just wanted a deep filled mince pie
with shortcrust pastry - or is that all-butter pastry? Or maybe
a brandy infused mince pie, or maybe the flaked almond
covered mince pie, or maybe the iced mince pie, or maybe
a flaky pastry mince pie, or maybe a stick it in a pipe and
smoke it mince pie? See what happens when there is too
much choice? It just gets silly. Just for the record I still want a
mince pie - just one kind, and plenty of them.

If you live within a 5-mile radius of my house you will be
able to smell Christmas soaking from mid-November to early
December. This tradition started in early adulthood when
a dear friend of mine showed me how to make Christmas
cake and Christmas pudding from scratch. For two weeks
my house is filled with the aromas of cinnamon, brandy,
amaretto and mixed spice. So delicious are these puddings I
make enough to see us through to Easter. To ensure enough
fruit is soaked, every gravy boat, fruit bowl, and jug must
be unearthed in order to carry out this task. The secret is
soaking the poor fruits in as much booze as they can absorb.
I push mine to the limit. I can often be found hunched over
my various containers filled with fruit muttering "Drink my

pretties for you must be strong and infused" and pouring amaretto in by the litre.

Preparing food from scratch at Christmas found its way to the Christmas dinner. Thanks to the helpful suggestions by celebrity chefs I found myself sweating more than the Virgin Mary on the first Christmas Eve:

Roast potatoes - peel them, chop them, boil them, bang them, oil them, season them, cook them.

Carrots - Peel them, chop them, oil them, season them, cook them, turn them.

Cauliflower Cheese - Chop it , grate it, season it, cook it.

Sprouts - Wash them, peel them, boil them, season them, fry them.

Christmas dinner was becoming somewhat of a faff before I discovered a little secret... I was furious when I found out, all that effort, had I just known...

YOU CAN BUY CHRISTMAS DINNER ALL PRE-MADE FROM THE SUPERMARKET!

Now Christmas dinner looks something like this:

All Christmas dinner - open them, oven them.

That's it. Voila. It doesn't taste nearly as nice without all the elbow grease but in the sweet blissful aftermath of ease, a 5p mini Yorkshire pudding never tasted so good.

Whether it's pre-made or lovingly created from scratch, I am so pleased that there is one truth about food at Christmas I can rely on and trust:

CALORIES DON'T EXIST AT CHRISTMAS.

"Yes, I would like the large hot chocolate with an entire selection box sprinkled on top." "Yes, I would love to sample each of the 15 different types of mince pies my supermarket is offering in one sitting (so I can make an educated choice as to which one to buy)." "Ice cream or double cream on my pudding? I think you meant ice cream AND double cream." If clothes do not fit as well in the aftermath of the merriment it is because they must have spontaneously shrunk and it is nothing to do with eating the selection boxes that were intended for your nieces and nephews. Chocolate only rots the teeth and mind - you were doing them a favour (says my rotten mind through my rotten teeth). Never in my tiny (rotten) mind would I ever consider devouring a six-course meal, but at Christmas it's customary. This is all thanks to the negative calorie rule - you chew more calories than you consume at Christmas - it's not magic, just science.

Oh Christmas, this break-up is starting to hurt. I am going to miss the freedom of saying, "Well, it's only Christmas once a year..." as I wash down my fourth green triangle Quality Street with a cherry brandy.

CHRISTMAS DRINK

"Drink at Christmas time has always been good."

Ever since that first promise of branded Tango at Christmas, my thirst for 'special' drinks this time of year has grown. Begone blackcurrant squash for if it does not fizz in one's mouth then it is not welcome upon my lips this festive season. Nowadays if it's not 40% proof it is not welcome upon my lips this festive season. There is no better time to drink, alcohol or not. Take mulled wine for instance. It is in fact merely red wine warmed up with added fruit and spice. Why do we not serve mulled wine all year round? Drinking mulled wine in January just seems wrong. Without the Christmas atmosphere it just seems like an added step to heat up wine when previously I could just drink it straight from the bottle. Christmas seems to force us into making extra special effort for the sake of Christmas. Usually, I would scoff at this extra effort but when it comes to Christmas drinks the extra effort pays off. Even coffee has been touched by Christmas magic and comes with honeycomb or gingerbread. Hot chocolates are served with lashings of cream and decorated with an entire tin of chocolates. These drinks alone can constitute as a meal in their own right. I once had a hot chocolate that was 850 calories and cost £12. The same calories and price as an entire margarita pizza. Just liquid calories - no chewing involved. Not that it matters of course as, thank goodness, calories are redundant this time of year.

Why is it excusable at Christmas to drink alcohol at any time of day? Now, I'm not an animal, there is a time and a place for the hard stuff, and that's every night as soon as my little darlings have made their way to the land of nod, but at Christmas time it's not frowned upon to partake in a mid day tipple. A little Buck's Fizz with breakfast, a mulled wine mid-day, an expresso martini before the bedtime routine, a peppermint whisky in the evening (whilst cleaning their Christmas presents). All perfectly acceptable and almost rude not to indulge in at this jolly time of year.

I am not happy about letting the Christmas magic go from my beverages. Cold wine in December, regular flavoured Irish cream rather than mint or salted caramel, hot chocolate without the added calories - oh, how undignified. You've ruined me Christmas, I am now scrabbling for the finer things. I am now seriously starting to question this break-up.

FAMILY AT CHRISTMAS

"Family was at the heart of Christmas wasn't it?"

As a child Christmas dinner was the one time our little family of five would sit down together at the table and eat. The other 364 days a year my siblings and I would eat separately to my mum and dad. Every year I was surprised at how wholesome and warming it was to sit with my parents. My mum would sit for 18 minutes, that included her pulling a cracker and handing out and opening table presents, before she was whipping away plates with the remains of nibbled sprouts. Before I knew it Mum had the cow bell in hand and was yelling "Christmas dinner is over! Christmas dinner is over for another year!" And that was that. Dinner together was indeed over for another 364 days. It may have only been 18 minutes, but those 18 minutes were my favourite 18 minutes of Christmas, and I thoroughly enjoyed all 18 of them.

"Family is still at the heart of Christmas isn't it?"

The sacred oath I took when becoming host on Christmas Day ensures each of my subjects under my roof enjoys our festivities to the fullest. Unbeknown to them, as subjects they also took an oath to follow the festive guidelines their dutiful host lays down for them. Following these rules will result in a productive, memorable and magical Christmas Day for all.

The first rule - Dress Code. I do appreciate that the festivities will take place in our slightly rundown, semi-detached house. However, this is no excuse not to dress your finest. Christmas is the one time of year where we require you to don your best outfits to merely stay indoors - feel free to accessorise with slippers of course.

Rule Two - Present Giving. As difficult as this may be to follow, what with excitement running high on the big day, please refrain from presenting gifts to the children without the host in attendance. We will lose track of who has given what, resulting in thank you card chaos.

Rule Three - Help Yourself. We trust our guests implicitly and would encourage you to keep yourself topped up with beverages. The fridge is, as always, stocked high with premium drinks, so please do not let yourself go dry as you will not be waited on.

Rule Four - Christmas Dinner. Christmas dinner will last for approximately an hour. Once seated you will remain so for the duration of the meal and followed merriment. Due to the close proximity of the table to the dining room walls no seat swapping or toilet breaks can be permitted. Your host will be situated at the corner nearest the kitchen and be free to serve you as required.

Ok, so I may have a few minor guidelines to ensure that Christmas Day flows smoothly, but I do so out of love for my family. I want them to have as much fun as I do. I love watching my dad and father-in-law bond over their joint distaste of our lack of garden decor and moss-filled guttering. I love watching my mum and mother-in-law comment on how filthy the compost bin is, or how I need new tea towels next year for Christmas. I love watching my brother time out with all this family socialising and take a sneaky phone break. I love watching my sister exchange outfit admiration with my nan-in-law. But the bit I cherish the very most is when everyone is sitting at that long, wonky dining table tucking into an oven-ready, luke warm, Christmas dinner. Everyone who I love the most in the world sitting together, waiting patiently for the one gravy boat between twelve to float their way.

Why we don't meet more often for a full sit down meal, I don't know. It seems like too much hassle to choose a date to suit everyone and choose what to eat. But at Christmas time - years of carving this tradition has come together so we don't have to think 'what are we eating?' and 'what day is it?'. The day is the 25th and the food is (oven-ready) turkey.

The very, very best thing about Christmas is family. The chaos of having everyone together, talking over each other, making polite small talk with each other, laughing with each other, this is the reason I now realise I can't break up with Christmas. It's too much to lose. But I can't continue on this journey either. If I was Mary asked to bring the saviour into the world, I'd have asked for a few terms and conditions. A few T's crossed and I's dotted. A few 'get out' clauses along the way. Mary was chosen for a reason - she was a pushover. No one wants to give birth in a stable (what with animals logging everywhere). No one wants to travel by donkey at the best of times let alone when heavily pregnant. No one wants the pressure of being impregnated with the baby Jesus without a sniff of foreplay. I'm not a pushover. We will do Christmas my way without the animal feces and with plenty of foreplay.

I sweep Christmas's hopeful, tired, chubby face. It doesn't look so bad, there is still some twinkle in those fairy lights, sparkle in those baubles and needles on those branches. Maybe we can make this relationship work.

"This time, Christmas, if you and I are going to do this, if we are in it for the long haul, things have got to change. I can't have Scrooge's Christmas ghosts following me around."

I can't have the ghost of Christmas past pressuring me with outdated traditions and standards of those traditions. Standards I admit I have set for myself and only have myself to blame for. Standards that are so ridiculously high no one in their right mind would even dream of them, yet live them. I wouldn't set these standards for anyone else, so why do I torture myself with them? But these traditions I have inherited and not requested. I have to refuse some of them if we are to continue this relationship. Christmas puts pressure on an already challenging schedule. We don't get an extra day in the week to manage the extra Christmas workload. Goodbye unwanted traditions, so long, ridiculous standards.

I can't have the ghost of Christmas present constantly guilting me into making Christmases more magical and more memorable for my children. The most memorable things for me as a child were the simple things; my family sitting down together to eat Christmas dinner, watching Christmas TV together with branded fizzy pop and a certain cheesy flavoured snack. I am so lucky to be in this position where I feel so overwhelmed at Christmas. I am so lucky to have to write out a Christmas calendar of events in October to fit everything in. I am so lucky to have a family to feel guilty about. But there is only so much guilt one person can take. I don't know how my mum made Christmases look so easy. I'm starting to wonder if they were more difficult than she let on. Perhaps the reason she did the Christmas shop in November was because the supermarket was quieter, perhaps she didn't enjoy putting up more string for my ever-flowing stream of Christmas cards, perhaps 'non gifts' were essential to bulking up a stocking when finances were tight. Guilt - you can go and fuck yourself. I know I do my best and maybe my best isn't perfect and worthy of the cover of 'Parenting at Christmas' magazine, but my best is good enough for the new me. Again, just so we are clear, fuck off guilt.

I can't have the ghost of Christmas future continually poking at me, pointing at how ridiculous Christmas is and how dreadful it is for the environment. Christmas is our past and our tradition, but eco living is the future of our planet. If Christmas is here to stay, eco living and Christmas are going to have to find some kind of harmony and peace with each other. We can start by scrapping Christmas cards, plus, my child doesn't need a stocking taller than her, and in future I will be the one brave enough to say "Shall we not do presents this year?". If I do my best to walk this new path of eco living I need you to know I will do so imperfectly, this is new and I will do my best. If I stumble please just help me up and point me in the right direction. I don't need a lecture, judgement or guilt ('cause I thought I had told you to fuck off guilt).

I felt elated, lighter, cleansed, more focused, like my house in January once I've taken the decorations down. Christmas and I are turning a new page, making a new start, enjoying a fresh beginning. If Christmas is willing to tame the three ghosts then I am willing to embark on this relationship with a new sense of ease and gratitude. I leapt into Christmas's arms. It felt warm and soft (despite the pine needles) and we were full of hope. Christmas didn't seem nearly as tall as what it once was, nor as wide - I wasn't engulfed by this embrace, it was inviting and familiar. As I brushed off the thick layer of glorious glitter from my chest I gave Christmas a cheeky grin. After everything I had just said we still wanted to be together and this time it would be different - we would make it work. We left the coffee shop full of cheer and excitement about the Christmases to come. Most importantly, we left the coffee shop as one.

Long distance relationships can work:

@breaking_up_with

www.breakingupwith.co.uk

weneedtotalk@breakingupwith.co.uk

Scan me to find out more about Breaking Up With:

Coming soon:

BREAKING UP
WITH
Holidays